'Tis Well...

The Life and Death of George Washington

By Jeffrey E. Finegan Sr. ~ Illustrated by Preston Keith Hindmarch

To Jack,
A future historian!
Best wishes!

2020

'Tis Well...

Siegle Books

Library of Congress Control Number: 2014909970
ISBN 978-0-9852819-4-6 (Hardbound) $18.95
ISBN 978-0-9852819-5-3 (Softbound) $12.95

First Printing 2014
Second Printing 2018

Printed in the USA

www.tiswell.net

Acknowledgments

While writing *'Tis Well* I considered myself very fortunate to have those who contributed so much to our first book, *Colonel Washington and Me*, to again play a huge role in our second effort.

~

First among those is my editor, Stephanie Nikolopoulos. Her prompting, guidance, and editing skills have made this experience as rewarding as the first one.

~

In a similar way but from a historic perspective Mary V. Thompson, research historian at Historic Mount Vernon, George Washington's home, has examined the text for historic accuracy with her incredible knowledge of all things Washington.

~

To have one of the top libraries dedicated primarily to the revolutionary period in ones backyard is truly an asset. The David Library of the American Revolution is an invaluable place to have access to and particular thanks goes to librarian Kathie Ludwig for her assistance while doing research there.

~

I would be remiss if I did not again mention Mary Ann McFadden who initially shepherded me through the process of bringing a book to market from the ground up. I am thankful for her sound advice that continues to be a guiding light.

~

My family's collection of Washington and early American manuscripts that are seen throughout the story would not have been remotely possible without Joseph Rubinfine.

~

Serving in inspirational roles and always very liberal with their time are Joe Garrera and lifelong family friend Lou Reda of Lou Reda Productions in Easton, PA. Thanks also to Tom Turner for sharing his printing expertise.

~

Without the art of Preston Hindmarch, the story would not come to life in the way that it does. His artistic talents do not stop with the images but extend to laying out the pages as you see them. Our many hours spent together in his shop discussing the poignant moments of the story and their relation to art and manuscript placement are truly rewarding and afford me the satisfaction of a personal imprint on the final result.

~

Thank you to all for making this second in a series on the life of George Washington possible.

Jeffrey E. Finegan Sr.
2014

www.tiswell.net

Preface

Seen through the prism of Washington's life long friend and personal physician, *'Tis Well* recounts George Washington's early life and frontier experience all the way to the history altering events that changed and shaped the world in which they lived and ultimately to the General's peaceful passing at his beloved estate, Mount Vernon.

As George Washington lay dying, he is surrounded by family, servants, and physicians. His ordeal is a day long process. Washington is resigned this day will be his last. He is well served by all who attend him – family and staff, free and enslaved. All promptly grant his every wish. Of those who have assembled that day, one person has known the General the longest and shared more hardships and experiences than any other, including his beloved wife Martha.

'Tis Well, The Life and Death of George Washington, the second in a series of books that explores the life and legacy of our nation's preeminent founding father, offers a distinctly different perspective than its predecessor, *Colonel Washington and Me*. Although the two books share similar highlights of Washington's life the two differ in that *'Tis Well* takes a deeper look into his family history and his early development and has a strong concentration on the last two days of the General's life and funeral.

Years after he witnesses his dear friend pass from this life into the next, Dr. James Craik recalls their collective sojourn in a letter to a friend who has asked for his reminiscence – from the early 1750s and the French & Indian War, through the long eight years of the Revolutionary War and ultimately to the creation of a new nation in the republican likeness that George Washington embodied.

As with *Colonel Washington and Me*, the incomparable art of Preston Hindmarch truly brings the story to life and historic architecture is once again a central theme. Eighteenth century manuscripts, in particular a letter written the day after Washington's passing, describing his death, are an important supplement to the art images. Additionally, I have elected to have all quotes appear with their original spelling, capitalization, and punctuation.

The Papers of George Washington as well as his diaries provide the majority of the information that allows us to create our story much as Dr. Craik would have told it. So join him as he recounts their incredible journey through history - all the way to the General's final hours within the comfort of his candle-lit bedroom.

This book is dedicated to my late father, James T. Finegan Sr.,
who lit the history fire in his three sons.

Chapter One

Alexandria, Virginia   December 14, 1809

Dear Sir,

     I had the honor of receiving your letter this day, and it is with a great degree of humility that I put in writing my recollection of my association with General George Washington and that fateful night he breathed his last. Of all those in attendance that evening, and I say this with a humble heart, I knew the General longer than anyone else who assembled that cold night of December 14, 1799, including Mrs. Washington. We fought together in two wars and nearly a third. We spent two thirds of our lives in common experience such as fox hunting, dinners at his Mount Vernon estate, and making our way to the Virginia frontier in search of fertile land that would one day be part of the expansion of this great nation. I had the distinct honor to serve as the Washington family physician for many years. I treated everyone from General and Mrs. Washington to extended family and the more than three hundred enslaved men, women, and children from Africa or of African decent who lived and worked at Mount Vernon. I considered him my oldest and dearest friend.

Our stories differ in that he was part of the third generation of Washingtons born here in Virginia, and I was a native of Scotland, emigrating here in the early 1750s. The colonies still belonged to the British Empire, and I arrived just in time to serve our British king, George II, in the French and Indian War. It was a lesser known Colonel Washington who actually gave the order to his troops to fire upon a small detachment of French soldiers and their Indian allies that began the war. It was about this time I met Colonel George Washington when we served together in the Virginian Regiment. From this very unique perspective, I recount our collective story and illustrate how a Virginian colonel and planter ultimately became the father of this great nation and one of the most famous men in the world.

The Washington saga began in the mid-1600s when his great-grandfather John came to the colony of Virginia and fell in love with the lovely Anne Pope. He decided to marry her and start a family here in the king's oldest dominion rather than return to

George Washington's journey to be the most famous man in the world began with his life as a surveyor. Thomas, Lord Fairfax introduced the young man to the frontier of Virginia, employing him as a surveyor and from here his military and political careers were born. This survey dated 1750 was hand written and drawn by an eighteen-year-old George Washington.

England. John had a son named Lawrence who in turn had a son of his own named Augustine. Augustine married a woman named Jane Butler, with whom he had several children. While Augustine took his sons Lawrence and Augustine Jr. to England for school, his wife passed away. Upon his return, he married Mary Ball, who on February 11, 1731/2, gave birth to their first son, George Washington.

Many a night at fireside, George shared with me his recollections of his earlier days. Unlike his older half-brothers, George never had the opportunity to travel to England to attend school or visit the family's beautiful estate at Sulgrave Manor. He did, however, consider himself a very loyal Englishman and was prepared to serve his king in whatever capacity required. As a child George shared his time between several farms that his mother and father called home. You will see, however, that his brother

'Tis Well...

Lawrence and the family estate at Little Hunting Creek presented the younger George with life-altering opportunities. Unfortunately Washington men did not live very long, and when George was eleven years old his father, Augustine Washington, passed leaving the young man with an overly protective mother. It may well have been to the benefit of the future nation that she forbade the fourteen-year-old lad from joining the British navy, as was his wish!

Chapter Two

None played as pivotal a role in Washington's development, though, than his brother Lawrence. Fourteen years his senior, Lawrence was active in Virginian politics and the British military. He also was a founding member of the Ohio Company, which was started by prominent men seeking to develop the Ohio Valley for commercial purposes. Residing at Little Hunting Creek in the story-and-a-half farmhouse built by

his grandfather and namesake, Lawrence, and his father Augustine, he was married to the daughter of a neighbor—but not just any neighbor. Not far from the Washington home was Belvoir, the grand estate of the Fairfax family. In a planter class that was very conscious of social standing, the union by marriage of the Virginian families was a step up for the Washingtons, who although land and slave owners, were second-tier Virginian aristocracy. It proved to be just the opportunity a young George would need for advancement. Virginians aspired to be all that their British cousins were. They reveled in their fine country estates, beautiful clothing, gardens, carriages, and anything their agents in England could return to them for the hog's heads of tobacco that they shipped. George Washington was exposed to all the world had to offer courtesy of his brother Lawrence and the Fairfaxes. Most important, however, was the young man's introduction to a Fairfax cousin, Thomas, Lord Fairfax, who was proprietor of millions of acres of Virginia land. Political alliances and ancient agreements in England sent men as "proprietors" to the colonies to "grant" land to those seeking it. The royal monarchy claimed everything from the Atlantic to the Pacific! Lord Fairfax had millions of acres under his supervision, and required a surveyor. He must have seen something promising in young George, even though he had never studied at the advanced level that his brothers and father had. George was proficient in mathematics and was, no doubt, to make a fine surveyor.

On July 20, 1749, George Washington became a licensed surveyor for Culpeper County, Virginia—it was his first oath of office. His commission was granted by the College of William and Mary in the colonial capital of Williamsburg and remained active until October 1752. In that short span of time he executed 190 surveys and acquired by purchase his first parcel of land. Known as the Bullskin Plantation, he would own it for the duration of his life. George began his lifelong love of farming here and this acquisition also started his unquenchable desire to obtain good land, a preoccupation that never left him. By the time his official surveying career ended he had acquired through either purchase or grant 2,315 acres of the nearly 70,000 he would have at the end of his life. He continued to survey privately for a lifetime, once taking advantage of a frozen Potomack River to obtain a proper angle on a parcel at Mount Vernon that had eluded him until nature offered him this unique opportunity. George and his enslaved valet Billy would often be seen about the Mount Vernon property and elsewhere with the General's surveying instruments. When Lord Fairfax passed in 1781, George wrote to Bryan Fairfax: "Altho the good old Lord had lived to an advanced age, I felt a concern at his death." At the time no one realized that the most important aspect of Washington's tenure as a surveyor was his introduction to the Virginian frontier and thus his knowledge of this remote area of the colony. It would prove to be of immeasurable importance to his future adventures.

The early 1750s supplied life-altering events for the young Virginian, although all were not readily apparent at the time. Lawrence was not well. It was decided he would benefit from a change of climate, and plans were made to travel to the island of Barbados. What better traveling companion to have than his brother George, who would certainly benefit from a trip to a stronghold of British-held islands? George would be exposed to the cultural and political elite who called this tropical paradise home. With travel plans in place the Washington brothers readied themselves for what was to be about a month long journey aboard ship. It was the end of September 1751 as their beloved Virginia faded in the distance. Lawrence had traveled to similar destinations while with the British military, but for young George it was a new world indeed. He consumed strange fruit—the pine-apple—saw his first coconut tree, likely attended the theater for the first time, and enjoyed the social life that an important

'Tis Well...

Fort Necessity, George Washington's hastily built garrison in the "Great Meadow" was the first of several military disasters that plagued his early career. As with all great leaders, he learned from his mistakes. He would one day own the land on which the fort sat.

island such as Barbados had to offer. They stayed for a couple of months before Lawrence elected to travel to the island of Bermuda for additional relief, as his health had not improved. Meanwhile, George boarded the ship Industry, and around December 19 was on his way home. George Washington would never leave the country again! Of all of his experiences on that trip, the one that stood out was his exposure to smallpox. He was in great discomfort for nearly three weeks with the communicable disease responsible for millions of deaths around the world. The good news was that once contracted, the disease provided lifelong immunity. Years later when the Continental Army was ravaged by smallpox, General Washington walked freely through camps and hospitals without fear. Once back in Virginia, at the request of folks in Barbados, George made a trip to the governor's mansion in Williamsburg, Virginia's capital, to deliver items to the royal governor, Robert Dinwiddie. When George applied for his first military position it was the same Governor Dinwiddie who reviewed the young man's credentials and no doubt recalled their first meeting on that cold January day.

Although being born to parents in the planter class of Virginia's ruling elite was an advantage only few enjoyed, one needed more than family ties to rise to the top. Two enormous opportunities were about to descend upon Washington, but they came at an incredible cost—the death of his beloved brother Lawrence. In July 1752, Lawrence finally succumbed to the lung ailment he had struggled with the past few years. First, George inherited the Washington family estate at Little Hunting Creek, now named for British admiral Edward Vernon. This more than doubled his land holdings, and in a few short years would become George's permanent home. Additionally, Lawrence's passing created a vacancy within the Virginia military establishment. The position of adjutant was not terribly important but once in that office opportunities for advancement were not far off. When Governor Dinwiddie read the young man's name as applicant, he surely recalled the tall Virginian he first met at his mansion earlier bearing deliveries from Barbados. On December 13, 1752, George Washington received his first military commission "to be Major and Adjutant of Militia, Horse and Foot." For all that he accomplished and for all that had come his

way he, no doubt, reflected on the sacrifice that those who had gone before him had made—his father and his brother Lawrence made all of this possible. George lived a long and event-filled life and would need additional help along the way. "Divine providence," as he often referred, would take him to heights never before seen on earth!

This piece of Virginian money not only bears a wonderful Coat of Arms of the colony but also the signatures of two prominent Virginians, Peyton Randolph and John Blair Jr. Lifelong residents of Williamsburg, both men knew Washington well from Randolph's service as Speaker of the House of Burgesses and President of the Continental Congress to John Blair's serving as representative for the College of William and Mary in the House of Burgesses to his signature on the Constitution. It warns the bearer that "to counterfeit is death."

Chapter Three

Pondering the serious nature of information he read in a letter from his superiors, Governor Dinwiddie knew tension with the French was escalating: "You are to require of them peaceably to depart. . . ." And if they did not, he was "to drive them by force of arms." The continent and the world were brought to the precipice of war! The French and English had been enemies for centuries. The French governor in Canada, the Marquis De Duquesne, desired to expand his king's presence on the North American continent. His hope was to link Canada with the Mississippi River via the Ohio Valley. At about the same time, the British Crown granted a half million acres to the Ohio Company of which prominent Virginians, including Dinwiddie, were investors. The perfect storm was on the horizon. A young George Washington had a case to make. Already wearing the uniform of a Virginian adjutant and familiar with the west from his surveying days, he argued that he would make a logical choice to visit the French commander. The time had come for the governor to act. He had no choice but to inform the invaders of his majesty's dissatisfaction with their incursion onto British soil and to ask him if he would care to leave peacefully or face military action. George was instructed on October 30, 1753, by his governor to approach the French commander and "in the name of his Britannic Majesty to demand and answer from him thereto." His dangerous journey to the frontier and return to Williamsburg with the French commander's response brought Washington almost instant fame.

The Capital Building in Williamsburg, Virginia was home to the House of Burgesses of which George was a member for sixteen years. It was from here and from this elected body that he was selected as one of the delegates to attend a "continental congress" which started him on the path to the national and world stage.

A few years prior, 1750 to be exact, I left my hometown of Arbigland, Scotland, and traveled to the West Indian Islands. Educated at the University of Edinburgh and trained for the medical service with the British Army, I began a new life in the western hemisphere. Not long thereafter I found myself practicing medicine in Norfolk, Virginia. It is about this time that my personal involvement and long endearing friendship with Washington began. The situation in the Ohio Valley was not improving and soon-to-be Lieutenant Colonel Washington was instructed to gather troops, equipment, and supplies, using Alexandria, Virginia, as his rallying point. I received my commission as surgeon to the group on March 7, 1754, and soon we were headed west!

On May 28, 1754, Washington and his men came upon a small gathering of French soldiers and their Indian allies at what is known today as Jumonville Glen in Pennsylvania. "We were advanced pretty near to them, as we thought, when they discovered us; whereupon I ordered my company to fire," he later wrote. The French and Indian War had begun! With the order to engage the enemy, the young Virginian had incited a war that would be fought around the world. His personal involvement lasted until 1758, and it was during that time we grew to be great friends. He was respected and admired by all who served under his command, and he ultimately attained the rank of colonel. Utterly fearless, he earned the name "Conotocarious" or "town taker" from the Indians for his exploits while in the heat of battle. With bullet holes in his coat and horses shot out from under him, his four years were ones of struggle and difficulty; his surrender of Fort Necessity, the annihilation of General Braddock and his troops, and the many attacks and murders of frontier families were only made worse when compounded with delays in the arrival of men, equipment, gun powder, clothing, and food. The war, however, vaulted him onto the national and world scene. His visit to Governor Shirley of Massachusetts had the populace of the cities of Philadelphia, New York, and Boston hoping to catch a glimpse of Colonel Washington of the Virginia Regiment. In Europe, his exploits dominated conversation in the coffee houses of London and Paris.

Greater yet was the education he received in the dealings of men—kings, governors, officers of superior and inferior rank, committees, and elected bodies. Would they help to mold and shape the man for some greater purpose or adventure in the future? George resigned his commission with his reputation intact and was the recipient of emotional farewell addresses from the men who served under his command as well as his colleagues in the Virginia House of Burgesses. In July of 1758 a seat representing Frederick County became open in Virginia's legislative body back in Williamsburg. Colonel Washington previously had run for the seat without success. This time some of us who were closely associated with him campaigned actively and our efforts were rewarded with his election. Retired from the military and now involved in Virginian politics his foundation continued to be built. Elected several times over he remained a burgess until shortly after being selected to lead continental troops in the Revolutionary War. George Washington remained a man of character when in one of his last addresses to his men he wrote: "For if I have acquired any reputation, it is from you that I derive it." For now he was happy to represent his people and his king.

Chapter Four

The 1750s were hard on George Washington. However, it had matured the young colonel in many ways. He was no longer the overly aggressive squire seeking adventure. The responsibility of sending young men into mortal combat made him wise beyond his years. Now a member of an elected assembly, he headed east to the capital of Williamsburg to retire from military life for what he thought, and hoped, would be the last time. Royal Governor Francis Fauquier no doubt accepted the Colonel's resignation that December 1758 with reluctance.

It was the Yuletide season, and Washington enjoyed the festivities that made Williamsburg a special place. Described by a friend as "measuring 6 feet 2 inches in his stockings," the young, retired colonel could not be missed as he moved hurriedly from shop to shop on the capital's main thoroughfare, Duke of Gloucester Street. He, no doubt, exchanged wishes for health and prosperity as the year closed. "His demeanor at all times composed and dignified. His movements and gestures are graceful, his walk majestic, and he is a splendid horseman," his friend continued. He was not the

In 1772 George Washington hand wrote and signed this two page letter to the Reverend Jonathon Boucher. Still the loyal British subject Washington writes that he prefers his money be invested in England where he is getting a return of five percent.

only one who noticed. A lovely young widow had taken notice of the colonel's many attributes. A few of us in the regiment knew this might be his reason for retirement, and as we begged him to stay we knew our motives were self-serving. Widowed at twenty-five years, Martha Dandridge Custis was a bright Virginian and mother of two young children, a daughter named Patsy and a son named Jackie. Martha and George had met earlier that year, and Colonel Washington had called upon her on several occasions at her home, eventually asking for her hand in marriage. She agreed and a date was set. With gifts purchased for his young bride and toys for little Patsy and Jackie gently tucked away, Washington headed out of Williamsburg and into a new phase of his life.

January 6, 1759, the last day of the Twelve Days of Christmas, the young couple became husband and wife. I am fairly certain that on that joyous day neither imagined they would someday become the president and first lady of a new nation. For now the title of husband and father was Washington's eagerly embraced top priority. He also assumed the responsibility of managing the estate of Daniel Parke Custis, Martha's late husband who died suddenly. The enormity of the estate immediately made George one of the wealthiest men in the colony, and with that came increased responsibilities such as being a vestryman at the local Anglican parish, executor of estates, lender of money to associates in need, and master to hundreds of Custis slaves. The children's affairs also needed to be managed, and Washington paid particular attention to Jackie's education. These and other issues kept the newlywed couple at Martha's home on the Pawmunkey River or her residence in Williamsburg. Then on April 5, 1759, George sent his servant Miles north to Mount Vernon with a note for his manager there "that I expect to be up tomorrow . . . You must have the House very well cleand . . . you must also get the Chairs and Tables and have them very well rubd & Cleand—the Stair case ought also to be polished in order to make it look well." He was bringing his new family home, and he needed to make a good impression. From this point on, he would forever be linked to this estate; Mount Vernon becoming an extension of the man himself.

Perhaps no man, maybe with the exception of Mr. Jefferson, is identified more with his property than is George Washington. He spent some time at Mount Vernon as a child but was mostly absent when he served the colonies during the French and Indian War. Now it was to become his permanent home. He wrote to a friend that no other estate in the country was more pleasantly situated. On more than one occasion he used the old biblical expression that he would prefer to be home under his own vine and fig tree. Many others also called Mount Vernon home. White servants, including farm managers, gardeners, and overseers, chose to live there. At any given time, more than three hundred black individuals were enslaved there. Most worked the five farms that comprised the agricultural portion of the property, however there were also seamstresses, carpenters, masons, blacksmiths, cooks, and individuals who played an important role in the daily operation of the property. The mansion house was the center of Mount Vernon, and the enslaved individuals who worked in the house were deemed more important than those laboring in the farms. Valets, butlers, and maids worked directly with the Washingtons and represented the family to the many guests who visited the estate over the years.

Mount Vernon was expanded on two occasions and it eventually included a small village of outbuildings to support a thriving community. The servants' hall, kitchen, laundry, and the stable were separate but

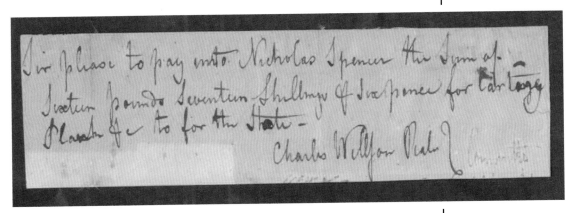

accessible from the main house. The grounds also featured kitchen gardens, pleasure gardens, orchards, and pastures. Crops grown on his farms were processed in his sixteen-sided barn and then sent off to the grist mill for the finished product. Other grain was sent off to the distillery. Fish from the Potomack River were salted and sold or used on the estate. A smokehouse was responsible for the tasty Virginia hams that Mrs. Washington was so proud to serve at her dinner table. The property abounded in livestock—cattle, sheep, pigs, chickens, horses, and mules. One year, around Christmas, he even had a brief visit from a camel—a real oddity for those of us living in Virginia. Nature supplied its own visitors to the estate as the forests abounded with deer and wild turkey. Many hours were spent at the General's favorite sport—fox hunting. I can still envision his enslaved valet Billy Lee serving as "huntsman," leading the charge with the estate's many fine hunting dogs eagerly showing us the way. I was very fortunate to be a frequent visitor on both official business, as one of the family's physicians, as well as one of Washington's closest friends. During our time of leisure, we watched from his veranda as sailing vessels made their way to and fro on the Potomack River.

Future public duties would take George and Martha away from their beloved home for a total of sixteen years, but for now they were happy to settle in as a family. Although they had no children of their own, George and Martha spent a long and

'Tis Well...

In 1770 Dr. Craik and George Washington are in search of the spoils of war. During the French and Indian War the crown used as an incentive to join the army the promise of land in the event of a favorable outcome. The two men assumed the responsibility of looking for good land for themselves and the men with whom they served

fruitful life there raising Martha's two children and two of her grandchildren. Washington loved his stepchildren, and they loved and revered him in return. Sadly, neither of the children lived past the age of twenty-seven. When Jackie passed away, it was decided that two of his children would live with their mother in Maryland and two would call Mount Vernon home.

Although separated, the four remained very close throughout their lives. The two who lived on the estate, Nelly Custis and George Washington Parke Custis, have very fond memories of life with their grandmother and beloved step-grandfather.

The Washingtons did a fair amount of traveling, mainly to Williamsburg for the General Assembly. I was a guest on a trip to the warm springs in the western part of the colony, and in 1770 Colonel Washington and I traveled in search of lands to be distributed to us and fellow members of our regiment for our service during the war. George eventually owned the land where his ill-fated Fort Necessity was located. Both of us had been there under difficult circumstances, but now the meadow was a beautiful place to visit. It was during these experiences that our friendship grew even closer. Although a quiet member of the House of Burgesses, Washington was slowly becoming one of the more prominent and respected men in the colony of Virginia.

Chapter Five

We hoped the forthcoming decade would be one of boundless exploration west and a time of peace. Sadly, 1760 was marked by the passing of King George II. Proud to call ourselves British subjects, we had served our king during the French and Indian War. Our hopes were renewed with the coronation of his grandson, twenty-two-year-old George III. A postwar depression made life difficult for some, but as we celebrated with balls and illuminated public buildings, we were certain our new king would lead us forward. Colonel Washington's farms were now operating to his liking with his products being sold both here and in England. In return came the

many barrels and crates of goods that were difficult to find here in the colonies but were readily available from merchants in the British Isles. He once wrote to a correspondent that he preferred his money be invested in England!

Mid-decade, a progression of politically inspired events aroused our senses and had us taking note that something was amiss with the relationship between England and her thirteen colonies in the New World. Beginning with the Stamp Act, England levied a series of taxes aimed at the inhabitants of the colonies. The monarchy said this was to pay for our protection and expenses incurred during the French and Indian War, but we colonists objected to being taxed by a government which allowed us no elected representation in Parliament. Tension mounted until blood was finally spilled in 1770 at what has become known as the Boston Massacre. After a confrontation with British regulars five citizens lay dead in the street. Finally, in 1774 delegates from all thirteen colonies met at Carpenters Hall in Philadelphia, Pennsylvania, for the first Continental Congress. The delegates discussed the current state of political affairs. Without concluding on the need for immediate action to be taken in regard to the colonies' relationship with England, the delegates voted to adjourn with the provision that they would meet again next year. George was in attendance at the first gathering and was, once again, voted by his fellow burgesses to attend a second gathering. By the time the delegates arrived in Philadelphia for the Second

The signature of King George III adorned many official documents produced by his court.

The Coat of Arms of King George III. As a loyal British subject Washington knew this to be a symbol of the authority of the crown. Virtually all public buildings in the colonies displayed the King's emblem as a constant reminder of his power and authority.

'Tis Well...

Continental Congress their country was already at war!

In April 1775 we had read in horror that some of our fellow colonists and British regulars lay side by side in death in the small Massachusetts towns of Concord and Lexington. It seems that British troops had moved out of Boston in search of what they claimed were illegally stored weapons and ammunition that could one day be used against them. On quiet country roads, British soldiers and colonial militia exchanged blows. No one really knows who fired the first shot. The Revolutionary War had begun, and our lives were about to change forever.

Chapter Six

Crucial times required crucial decisions. The Boston Army was now in a standoff with our own British soldiers, and Congress believed they required the assistance of the rest of the colonies. To aid them Congress established a Continental Army. On June 15, 1775, George Washington was commissioned to lead the newly formed army

Although it suffered terribly at the Valley Forge encampment, the Continental Army came out of that winter with a new fighting spirit. The Issac Potts house served the General well during those desperate days.

in the rebellion against George III. It was a dangerous task, but we felt it our duty to defend our rights as Englishmen—even to the death. Washington wrote previously to a friend, "it is my full intention to devote my life and fortune in the cause we are engaged in, if need be . . ." The weight of the rebellion would rest on one man's shoulders.

The next eight years were ones of struggle, frustration, tragedy, and personal sacrifice. My friend General Washington proved to be a most incredible commander and leader of men. He was fearless in battle and surmounted obstacles presented by both the enemy as well as others who claimed to be patriots. He never waivered in his belief that the Almighty had ordained our cause and that future generations would benefit from our efforts. No sacrifice was too great. When he learned that his cousin and manager of Mount Vernon had given provisions to the crew of a British warship in the Potomack River during his absence he wrote that he would rather that they burned the house to the ground than aid them. Thus was his personal

commitment to the cause of liberty. He suffered grievous battlefield losses, but patriots will always remember his desperate efforts that kept the flame of liberty burning. His brilliant strokes defeated German mercenaries at the small New Jersey village of Trenton and British regulars at Princeton. Loyal officers like Henry Knox, Nathanael Greene, Alexander Hamilton, and the General's personal favorite, the Marquis de Lafayette, never relented in their commitment to the man himself. He was the beacon, the guiding light, that lit the path for all true patriots.

In 1777 I found myself back in uniform in the medical corps of the Continental Army. After the arrival of the French army, I worked closely with the Comte De Rochambeau, the French commander, who had come here to assist us along with the much needed French navy. Already enemies of the British, the French were more

than eager to join in the fight. Their navy provided us with invaluable service. I rose through the ranks, and by 1781 I was the chief physician and surgeon of the entire army. One of my major contributions to the cause was to warn General Washington of the Conway Cabal, a secret plot by several officers and members of

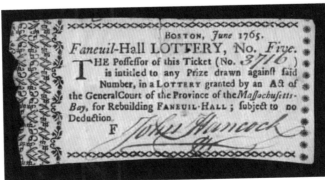

Congress to have him replaced as commanding general of the army. I learned of this terrible plot and informed my dear friend of its fiendish nature before it could have any adverse effect. Finally and in amazement, I witnessed the surrender of Lord Cornwallis' army at Yorktown, Virginia. This signified the end of the Revolutionary War even though the war was not officially concluded until the Treaty of Paris was negotiated and signed in Paris, France, in 1783. Victory was ours!

The Ford Mansion in Morristown, New Jersey was home to General Washington and his military family during the Revolutionary War amidst the severe winter of 1780. These encampments became more like home for the General after the arrival of Mrs. Washington.

One of the most recognized signatures in our nation's history, John Hancock was the first and only member of congress to sign the Declaration of Independence on July 4, 1776. Thirteen months previous his now famous signature adorned George Washington's commission from congress to be the commanding general of the Continental Army. This lottery ticket to rebuild Faneuil Hall was signed by him a decade earlier.

With the defeat of the largest and most well-trained army in the world and a peace treaty signed, General Washington did what few other victorious generals had done in the history of the world. He resigned his commission, returning it back to the Congress that issued it, and was a civilian once more. Christmas Eve 1783 he returned to Mount Vernon and his beloved family. His reputation had become even more distinguished as the man who had attained greatness and was willing to surrender it all for the simple life of a farmer. The Massachusetts Bay Assembly put it best when they wrote to General Washington, "may future generations, in the peaceful enjoyment of that freedom, the exercise of which your sword shall have established, raise the richest and most lasting monuments to the name of Washington."

Chapter Seven

After eight years on the battlefields of the Revolutionary War, Washington returned home as a private citizen and discovered Mount Vernon needed much in the way of work. He quickly began repairing the mansion and getting his farms back in order. My family and I moved from Port Tobacco, Maryland, to Alexandria, Virginia, and I began to visit Mount Vernon more frequently. The General, his enslaved valet William, and I now shared a special bond as a result of our years together in the Continental Army. While I had served in the medical corps, William had almost never left Washington's side during those eight long and trying years, and they had an incredibly close relationship. William's unyielding dedication to George during the war earned him his immediate freedom at the time of his master's passing. He was the only slave to receive that distinction.

The printed back portion of a Revolutionary discharge warns the soldier released from service that in the absence of a treaty of peace he is considered to be on furlough and may be called back in to the army. It bears the printed signature of "His Excellency" General Washington, as he was known to his men.

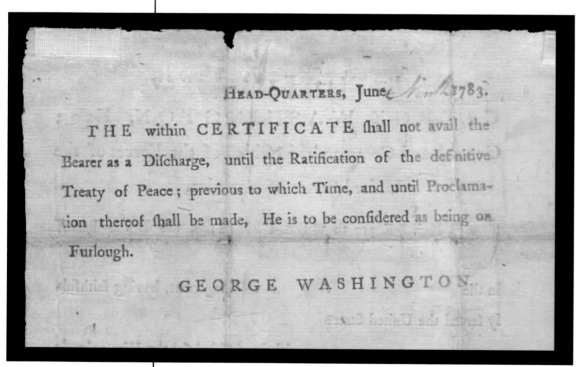

HEAD-QUARTERS, June ____ 1783.

THE within CERTIFICATE shall not avail the Bearer as a Discharge, until the Ratification of the definitive Treaty of Peace; previous to which Time, and until Proclamation thereof shall be made, He is to be considered as being on Furlough.

GEORGE WASHINGTON

After the war, Mount Vernon became the focal point for what was to come next as the colonies looked to the fearless general for further leadership. The Articles of Confederation only loosely bound the thirteen states together, and a small group that met at Mount Vernon determined that there needed to be a larger, more formal gathering of men who could solidify what was gained from the Revolution. Ultimately, they devised the Constitutional Convention, in which delegates from twelve of thirteen original colonies came to Philadelphia for four long hot months to map out a new government, one that created a more perfect union. Who better to be the Convention's president than George Washington? The formation of the government we live under today came out of those secret meetings. The new plan would consist of three parts: The legislative branch would consist of elected members of congress, who would serve certain terms. They would make the laws. The judicial branch would be comprised of shrewd men who would be appointed to serve for life. They would interpret the Constitution and see that the law was dispensed equally. Finally, the executive would be a single individual who would be elected by the people and serve in their best interest and also serve as the commander in chief of the armed forces of the country. We had just rid ourselves of the king. Could we now trust one person with this enormous amount of power and responsibility? As the men attending the convention looked to the front of the room, they saw the answer to that question sitting in the president's chair. Wise and powerful yet humble, George Washington fit the requirements of the type of executive the delegates sought.

Chapter Eight

Hearing carriage wheels on a quiet day in April 1789, George Washington glanced outside to find an old friend and fellow patriot stepping from his coach. The arrival of Charles Thomson, the longtime secretary of Congress, could mean only one thing. My dear friend would once again leave behind the estate that he loved and lead the country —this time as president. He accepted the role reluctantly, though. George was no longer the young man he once was and said that he was not up to the task at hand. Even though George felt he had already done his duty, his country needed him and he never waivered in his commitment to its people. Washington was inaugurated in New York City and spent the first year in office there. The capital moved in 1790 to Philadelphia, where he concluded both his first and second term. President Washington was able to visit home more than during the Revolution but he still longed for home and retirement.

There were many challenges to leading a fledgling nation, especially as there was no previous example of how a president should act. He knew he was setting the standard for future presidents for

Familiar to all those who served in Congress was the handwriting and signature of long-time secretary Charles Thomson. He was only one of two people to sign the Declaration of Independence on the fourth of July. It was in the spring of 1789 that he made the long journey from New York to Mount Vernon to inform George Washington he had been elected as the first president of the new nation.

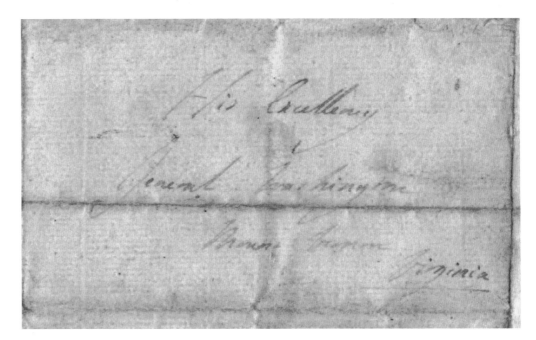

The first of two triumphant returns to North America by the Marquis De La Fayette following the American Revolution came in 1784. Landing in New York he immediately began his anxious journey to Mount Vernon to be reunited with the man he loved and admired most – George Washington. While in Philadelphia he wrote to his adopted father and allowed his emotions to flow, writing "there is no Rest for me Untill I get to Mount vernon—I long for the pleasure to embrace you, My dear General, and the Happiness of Being once more with You will be so great that No words Can Ever Express it . . ."

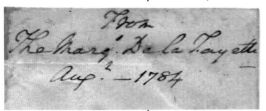

These images are of the address leaf of that letter with La Fayette writing to "His Excellency General Washington, Mount Vernon, Virginia." Upon receipt of this effusive letter George Washington dockets, "From the Marquis De la Fayette Aug. – 1784"

centuries to come. Furthermore, even though the country was no longer at war with England, it faced internal conflicts. In 1791, the Whiskey Rebellion, in which farmers in western Pennsylvania protested taxes, broke out. Finally, in 1794 Washington had to lead troops against the nation's own citizens to quell the rebellion. Serving in his administration were some of the brightest and knowledgeable men in the country, notably Alexander Hamilton and Thomas Jefferson. When Hamilton and Jefferson were not seeing eye-to-eye, the president decided the three of them should take a fishing trip off of the coast of New Jersey to reconcile. Just imagine these three incredible men in the same boat! For me my private medical work continued and I joined President Washington for his birthday celebrations in Alexandria as well as continued visits to Mount Vernon when he was home.

Although political divisions made his life difficult, he relished in a project that bore his name—the creation of the city of Washington. The Congress decided the new and permanent capital would be on the Potomack River, just north of where we both lived. Washington played a pivotal role in the establishment of the new city. He personally laid the cornerstone for the Capitol building and selected the location, architect, and plans for the President's Mansion. The city would in many ways bear his personal imprint. His adoptive son, Lafayette, thought him to be the "patriarch" of liberty and even sent him the key to the Bastille, the renowned prison in Paris, France, after ordering its demolition. Who better to oversee the construction of the new city?

During the time the Washingtons lived at the capital in Philadelphia many who visited the presidential residence could not help but notice something that made them uneasy. While in the capital and visiting the father of freedom it could not be overlooked that President and Mrs. Washington's many servants were virtually all enslaved people of African decent. Although they served the family well and made the first couple feel much like they did at home, some visitors had difficulty reconciling that these servants lived in bondage and were considered the personal property of the Washingtons. In fact, many slaves were now working to build the new capital. Well, little did those visitors know that the topic was weighing heavy on the president's heart and mind, as well. He was ready for the next phase of his life.

Chapter Nine

A cold and blustery day in Philadelphia, March 4, 1798, was George Washington's last as a public servant, with the exception of the time he spent preparing for a war with France that never materialized. Already known as the "modern Cinncinatus" for his desire to return to his farm like the Roman general had, George could not wait to retire. He stood silently that day, the day he solidified his reputation as the greatest man who lived as he watched and listened to John Adams take the oath of office as the second president of the United States. The new government was on a firm footing, his job was done. Following the ceremony, he walked by himself to his residence, where a crowd had gathered. With tears streaming down his cheeks, he turned and bowed to them one last time.

Washington's retirement from the presidency and his trip home were as celebrated as his journey to be inaugurated. At every stop enroute to Mount Vernon the citizenry appeared to see the retired president and hero of the American Revolution. Artillery under the command of Captain James Hoban, the architect of the President's

The City of Philadelphia played a prominent role in the formation of the new nation. Its City Tavern was host to the many visiting delegates who travelled to attend the Continental Congress, the Constitutional Convention, and ultimately as congressmen, senators or judges when the new government moved there in 1790.

Mansion, roared as my good friend's carriage passed both the new Capitol building and the future residence of the president in the city named for him. Traveling home with George was Mrs. Washington, her granddaughter Nelly, as well as George Washington Motier Lafayette, son of the Marquis de Lafayette, who had come to live with the Washingtons during the Reign of Terror in France. Washington and the Marquis de Lafayette had forged an incredible relationship during the war. The Marquis was probably the closest Washington ever came to having a son. I recall at the Battle of Yorktown giving explicit orders to all surgeons under my command to pay special attention to him in the event he was wounded.

Left behind in Philadelphia was Tobias Lear, Mr. Washington's secretary, and my son, George Washington Craik, who worked as one of the president's house managers, to finalize the family's move. In a postscript to a letter written to Mr. Lear after his departure, George humorously wrote, "On one side I am called upon to remember the Parrot, on the other to remember the dog. For my own part I should not pine much if both were forgot." I forwarded a note to my dear friend inviting him and his group to join us in Alexandria to be honored by the citizenry. He stopped briefly to greet us, but noted in his diary that, at long last, he was home for dinner by 4:00pm.

Presidential household receipt bearing the name of one of President Washington's house managers who was also one of the nine Craik children. Doctor Craik honored his old friend by naming his son George Washington Craik.

18. May 1796

Received of Geo. W. Craik One Hundred and Seventy One Dollars & 62/100 to purchase Sundries for the Presidents' Household —

$171 62/100

Fred[k]. Kitt

Chapter Ten

Although the former president was gratified to be home, he remained involved in the nation's progress. He traveled to Philadelphia in 1798 for several weeks preparing for war with France and occasionally stayed overnight in Georgetown. The development of the new federal city was important to him, and he greatly looked forward to the government moving there in the year 1800. On February 8, 1799, he noted in his diary that he "visited the Public Buildings" namely the Capitol and President's Mansion, which were still under construction. He was in near perfect health and had every reasonable expectation he would be in attendance at the ceremonies honoring him and the city that bore his name. Already, he had lived longer than all the men who came before him in his family tree.

The President's Mansion was not the only home being worked on. Although faithfully served by relatives and overseers during his absence, Washington's own house and most everything about it needed his attention. He wrote to former Secretary of War James McHenry, a fellow Virginian, "I have not one building or scarcely anything else about me that does not require considerable repairs. In a word I am already surrounded by Joiners, Masons, Painters & ca."

With the Washingtons now permanently at Mount Vernon, the frequency of my visits became greater in both a social and professional manner. In April 1799 serious illness afflicted Mr. Tobias Lear, who had by then returned from Philadelphia. He had originally been hired following the Revolutionary War when Washington came to the realization that he needed a permanent secretary to assist him at Mount Vernon. Benjamin Lincoln, a general from the late war, had highly recommended Mr. Lear, knowing that the New Hampshire native and recent graduate from Harvard would serve Washington well. Mr. Lear holds the distinction of being the first presidential secretary. George relied on him in many different circumstances, and Mr. Lear seems to have satisfied him in all regards. In addition to his secretarial duties, Mr. Lear acted as tutor to the Custis grandchildren. He lived more as a member of the family than simply a member of the staff, and fortunately he recovered from his illness and was able to continue aiding the family. He is known best for his faithful and unyielding service to George Washington especially in the General's final hours. Mr. Lear revered George Washington, once writing, "A complete knowledge of his honesty, uprightness, and candor in all his private transactions has sometimes led me to think him more than a man."

In September, a few months after Mr. Lear had fallen ill, Mrs. Washington was not well for an extended period. I occasionally spent the night at the mansion house in the event that my services were hastily required. Needless to say the General was relieved when she recovered.

In retirement the Washingtons went about their daily tasks. Assisted by his enslaved valet Christopher, the General rose early, ate a quick breakfast, and then rode on horseback to inspect his five farms at Mount Vernon. He would be back at three o'clock to the mansion house, where family and guests joined him. Mrs. Washington took great pride in managing the household. She oversaw the domestic staff and made sure they kept up with preparing meals, doing laundry, keeping the mansion tidy, and all the other many tasks that needed to be accomplished each and every day. The enslaved staff not only toiled for the Washingtons but also for the hundreds of visitors and overnight guests who came to the most famous estate in the country. In one year alone there were over six hundred overnight guests who lodged at Mount Vernon, prompting George to refer to his home as "a well resorted tavern." As they grew older, he wrote a favorite nephew to see if he would be willing to come to the estate and assume some of the entertaining duties, adding "as both your aunt and I are in the decline of life . . . it is my inclination to retire either to bed, or to my study, soon after candle light." It was an incredible amount of work for the servant staff which was made up chiefly of enslaved Africans or those of African decent. All worked diligently for the Washingtons and, although treated with respect, still found themselves living in the dark shadow of bondage.

Chapter Eleven

The century that had seen so much in the way of turmoil and political upheaval was rapidly coming to a close. We witnessed two great revolutions, ours as well as the French Revolution in 1789. The year 1799 was a busy and exciting one for the Washingtons. I saw George in January when he made a trip to Alexandria to become legal guardian for Martha's granddaughter Nelly, who was to wed George's nephew Lawrence Lewis. With her father deceased, Nelly selected her beloved step-grandfather to be at her side as she descended the grand staircase at Mount

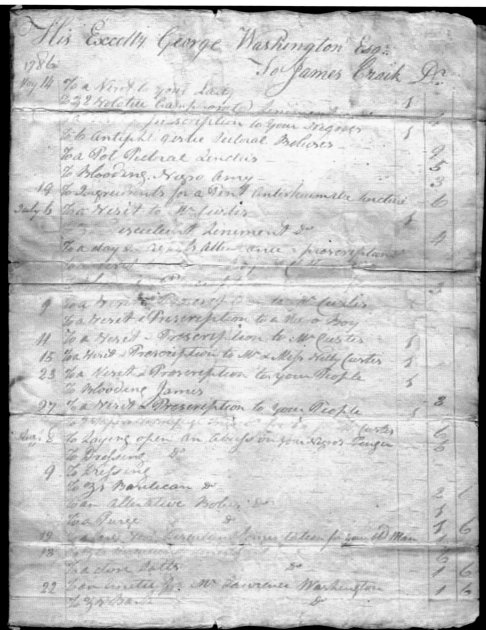

Doctor Craik bills George Washington for services rendered. Long the physician for the Mount Vernon estate, the document lists the many and varied people in need of his medical expertise – from the General and Mrs. Washington to slave Daphne who was in labor.

Vernon on her wedding day. The bride was beautiful in her wedding gown, and all in attendance were in awe as the General appeared in his old war colors of blue and buff. After all those years, he still proudly wore the uniform. It was no accident that Nelly picked February 22 to be wed. It was George Washington's birthday! He noted in his diary that night that ". . . Miss Custis was married abt. Candlelight. . . ." Actually we celebrated his birthday on two dates. The Washington family bible notes George was born on February 11. In the early 1750s the British empire, including its colonies, replaced the Julian calendar with the Gregorian calendar. As a result George's original birth date of February 11 was moved forward by eleven days; thus February 22 has commonly been recognized as his birth date. A week and a half before Nelly's wedding, General and Mrs. Washington were guests of honor at his last birthday celebration of the century in my hometown of Alexandria. George noted in his diary that he "went up to Alexandria to the celebration of my birth day. Many manoeuvres were performed by the uniform corps and an excellent ball and supper at night."

He returned to Alexandria frequently that year, notably for the horse races in May and as the guest of honor at our young nation's celebration of independence on July 4. The summer was hot and exceedingly dry. My good friend was very much concerned about his crops and the impact a poor harvest wrought on the Mount Vernon community. In a letter to his nephew Robert Lewis, dated August 17, 1799, the General's frustration overflowed in two respects. The aforementioned difficulties with his farm seem to have reached a fever pitch. "the drought has been so excessive on this estate, that I have made no oats—& if it continues a few days longer, shall make no corn. I have cut little or no grass, and my meadows, at this time, are as bare as the pavements."

There seemed to be a certain gravity to his countenance that went beyond the usual concerns that accompany life on the farm. In fact, my son George Washington Craik dined with the Washingtons on July 12 and mentioned that although polite and attentive to his guests the General seemed to be occupied with thoughts that went beyond dinner conversation. None of us knew at the time, but three days prior, in the privacy of his study—and I might add, in perfect health—George Washington wrote his last will and testament. The man could certainly look back on his life and see his great accomplishments for mankind. Perhaps there was something that had caused him to reflect and add new items that were not in the older will he had written at the time of the Revolutionary War. Did he have one last battle to fight for mankind?

After all these years, Washington had come face-to-face with the realities of slavery. In the same letter to his nephew in which he had written about the drought, he wrote: "It is demonstratively clear, that on this estate (Mount Vernon) I have more working Negroes . . . than can be employed to any advantage in the farming system." He continued, "to sell the overplus I cannot, because I am principled against this kind of traffic in the human species . . . and to disperse the families I have an aversion. What then is to be done? Something must, or I shall be ruined." An answer to his question would have to wait.

A good rain on August 20 afforded a slight bit of hope for his crops, but Washington was still surrounded by "miserable looking corn" and "parched up meadows." As late summer turned to fall, cooler weather finally brought some relief. In September his concerns turned from his farm to Mrs. Washington who was experiencing serious health issues. I knew when I was summoned during the night by one of the Washingtons' servants that something serious was before us. Luckily Mrs. Washington recovered in a couple of weeks. As life returned to normal, the stream of visitors to the estate continued. A "remarkably fine" day in November brought out George's old surveying tools. He surveyed a parcel of his own property and that of his neighbor, John Gill. I visited several times in November namely to call on ill servants. I was summoned to the estate on November 27 on a happier occasion—the birth of a great-grandchild to Mrs. Washington. I assisted in the delivery of a healthy little girl born to Nelly. Frances Parke Lewis brought much joy to the estate and the family!

My adopted home of Virginia was a special place in December as holly sprigs began to appear in windowpanes. With all of the crops in and a winter's worth of firewood dried and stacked, we eagerly looked to the Christmas season and all of the mirth and merriment that accompanied it. A young tutor serving on a large Virginia plantation once remarked that "nothing is now to be heard of in conversation, but the balls, the fox-hunts, the fine entertainments, and the good fellowship, which are to be exhibited at the approaching Christmas." As George Washington readied his estate for his many holiday visitors there is no doubt that he was reflecting on his life and the passing century. Certainly he thought of the many people who played a role in his life—his parents, brothers, sister, his stepchildren, and the many officers and men who were casualties of the two wars in which we participated. And yet, there was so much to look forward to. The new capital named for him was to become home to the federal government shortly after the beginning of the new century. Correspondence at the end of the year consisted of a wide variety of topics from pigs and fruit trees to a lengthy document reevaluating his farms and their supervision. The year 1800 would see much tighter management from fencing to barns to what the animals slept on. He was to personally assume oversight of three of his five farms. It was an aggressive plan for someone of his age and esteem, and he was up to the challenge! He never lost his interest in national matters. One of his

'Tis Well...

After completing his daily ride of his five farms at Mount Vernon, George Washington returns to the mansion house for dinner at three o'clock with family and guests. This day's ride would be his last. The result of his exposure to snow, hail and a "settled cold rain" would shock the nation.

last letters was to former Revolutionary War officer and the first Secretary of the Treasury, Alexander Hamilton, regarding the establishment of a military academy for the young nation.

Chapter Twelve

Throughout history, events of great magnitude have been foretold by strange or significant weather phenomena. On the night of December 12, 1799, George Washington routinely entered into his diary his remarks regarding the weather: 33 degrees in the morning, 28 at night, wind at the north east. He noted that at "about 1 oclock it began to snow—soon after to hail and then turned to a settled cold rain." More ominous, however, was an observation he made the evening prior. He entered into his diary a note that has stayed with me through the years: "A large circle around the moon last night." Was this lunar occurrence a foreshadowing of some calamitous or great event?

Only Mr. Lear knew at the time that during the hours of one and three on the afternoon of the twelfth while the General was inspecting his five farms, as was his daily habit, he was exposed to the bad weather he described in his diary. Mr. Lear observed that upon returning to the mansion house for dinner George had snow in his hair and that his collar was wet. Instead of drying his hair and changing into a new shirt, he rushed to complete some work with his secretary before dinner. He was always concerned about punctuality and did not want to keep his guests and family waiting.

The events over the next forty-eight hours were to astonish the nation and the world. I humbly submit that I played a role in what was to come.

When George rose on the thirteenth of December, he had a sore throat resulting from his exposure to the weather the previous day. This prevented him from following his daily routine. He did leave the house in the late afternoon, after the snow stopped, to mark a couple of trees that he desired to be cut down. Time in his study found him penning a letter to his farm manager, James Anderson. He spent the evening in the company of Mrs. Washington and Mr. Lear. His secretary noted that despite his health setback earlier that day George was in good spirits and amused himself by reading aloud from a newspaper when he

Molly, Caroline and Charlotte observe the General's final hours. They are in the room when Washington breathes his last. When Caroline arrives in the morning to start the Washington's fire she is alerted by Mrs. Washington that George is not well. Her hasty exit to seek assistance begins the day long saga that concludes with the General's passing. Washington's death means eventual freedom for 123 of his slaves and only William, his former valet, is granted immediate emancipation.

found something humorous or of interest. Mr. Lear suggested that he take something for his sore throat prior to bed, but George preferred to "let it go as it came." All seemed normal as he retired for the evening. In his diary that night, he wrote: "Morning snowing & abt. 3 inches deep. Wind at No. Et & Mer. at 30. Contg. Snowing till 1 Oclock and abt. 4 it became perfectly clear. Wind in the same place but not hard. Mer. 28 at night." These are likely the final words written in his long and adventurous life.

Early on the morning of Saturday, December fourteenth, I was startled by an urgent knock at my door. George personally sent one of his servants to me whenever someone at Mount Vernon was ill. So when I saw instead one of Mr. Lear's servants, Charles, before me, I understood the seriousness of the situation. Hastily opening the note he carried from Mr. Lear, my worst fears were realized. George was seriously ill and Mr. Lear asked that I proceed to Mount Vernon with all the swiftness my horse could carry me. I had made the trip easily on so many previous occasions, but on that cold December morning the ride past the snow-covered countryside and the flowing Potomack River seemed to take forever.

I arrived just around nine in the morning and was quickly briefed on the situation. George had awoken at about three o'clock that morning with his sore

'Tis Well...

Unlike most revolutionaries in history, George Washington dies peacefully in his own bed. The warmth of the candlelight emanating from the Washington's bedroom is set against the cold December night. It is late on the evening of the fourteenth and the greatest of all American heroes is about to breathe his last!

throat considerably worse. Mrs. Washington wanted to summon help immediately, but the General, fearing for her health, thought it best that she remain in bed. When servant Caroline arrived at daylight to start their morning fire she was sent immediately to alert Mr. Lear of George's condition. Mr. Rawlins, an overseer on the property who had a reputation for bleeding the servant population, was also summoned. "Bleeding" is a medical practice in which the patient has blood drawn in order to bring their body back to a state of balance. Mr. Rawlins arrived quickly and was very nervous about the task at hand. George, seeing this, urged him on and reassured him when he told him "don't be afraid." Mrs. Washington feared too much blood was being taken, but the General dismissed her fears and instructed the

'Tis Well...

procedure to continue. After being informed of all of this, I diagnosed his aliment as "quinsy," a severe inflammation of the throat. I directed the bleeding to continue and throughout the course of the day employed various internal and external remedies in an attempt to relieve his severely constricted throat. None seemed to provide the desired effect but the arrival around three o'clock of two additional physicians, Dr. Elisha Cullen Dick and Dr. Gustavas Brown, gave me some comfort. After they independently examined George, we repaired to the lower level to discuss his condition and what might be done about his serious circumstance. Dr. Dick, the youngest of the three of us, proposed a new medical procedure in which the General's trachea would be opened to relieve pressure on his throat and allow him to breathe more comfortably. Ultimately it was decided he was in no condition for a procedure of that magnitude. Bleeding and topical applications continued but none seemed to have any positive effect. At four o'clock George became restless and requested that Martha, who had not left his side, go to his study and retrieve two wills that she would find in his desk. She was to bring both to him. After examination he handed one back to her with the request that it be burned in the fire. The remaining one was to be used in the event of his death. She immediately placed it away for safe keeping. Also assisting the General during his ordeal was his valet Christopher, as well as house servants Caroline, Charlotte, and Molly. All were enslaved, had been with the Washingtons for years, and anxiously watched, knowing their fates were tied to his. Likewise Mr. Lear served faithfully throughout the day, and George confided in him more than any of us.

Shortly after the General reviewed his wills, Mr. Lear sat on the edge of the bed and took him by the hand. In a low voice the dying hero said to him, "I find I am going, my breathe cannot last long; I believed from the first that the disorder would prove fatal. . . ." At about five o'clock I came back into the room and went to his bedside. "Doctor," he said to me, "I die hard, but I am not afraid to go, I believed from my first attack, that I should not survive it, my breath cannot last long." I held his hand tightly but could not utter a word. Absorbed in grief, I retired to the fireplace. Several more attempts around eight o'clock failed to produce any results, and my colleagues again retired to the lower level. The Washington family considered me an intimate friend, and so I remained in the room with George, Mrs. Washington and Mr. Lear.

The final scene I am about to describe has been indelibly marked in my mind, and I recall it as though the occurrence were yesterday. After several attempts to speak, George said to Mr. Lear, "I am just going! Have me decently buried; and do not let my body be put into the vault in less than three days after I am dead." Mr. Lear, unable to speak, nodded. Desiring to be sure his final commands were heard, he asked his secretary, "Do you understand me?" Mr. Lear answered yes, and to that my oldest and dearest friend of fifty years spoke the final words of his incredible life responding "Tis well."

Somewhere between ten and eleven o'clock George became completely relaxed, his breathing no longer a struggle as Mr. Lear held his hand to comfort him. We all observed the General as he withdrew his hand and checked his pulse. As he was doing so, his hand collapsed to the bed. Mr. Lear reached and immediately drew George's hand near to him and my impulse was to close his eyes. We were with him as he breathed his last breath. The great Washington had passed from this life into the next. We stood silently, not quite comprehending what our eyes had seen. Mrs. Washington broke the silence: "Is he gone?" Unable to speak, Mr. Lear held up his hand in assent. She could only repeat his words saying "'Tis well, all is now over. I shall soon follow him. I have no more trials to pass through." The following day, Tobias Lear wrote to George's nephew William A. Washington that "He died as he had lived—Fortitude in extreme pain and Composure at his latest breath never left him, and he retained his reason to the last moment."

I regained my composure and sent for my fellow doctors to come to the

'Tis Well...

As longtime secretary to General Washington, Tobias Lear had the task of telling the world that George Washington was no more. The previous night he held the General's hand as he spoke the final words of a long and fruitful life - "Tis Well." On December 15, 1799 Lear awoke at Mount Vernon and wrote twelve letters announcing the great man's death. President John Adams and Alexander Hamilton are among those receiving notification. This letter was written to George Washington's nephew and executor William Washington. In it Lear mentions that, amongst others, Doctor Craik was in attendance caring one last time for his old and dear friend.

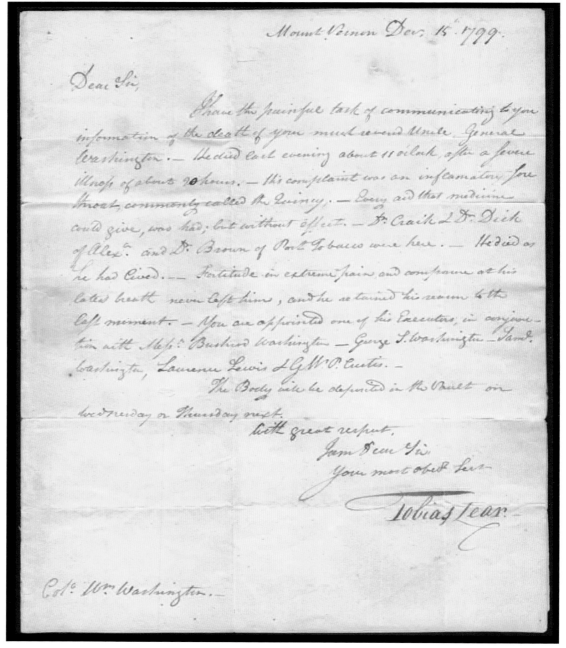

bedchamber one last time. They too stood silently and bid farewell to America's first hero. At around midnight Washington's lifeless body was taken to the east end of the house, where his tall frame was laid out with great reverence. Due to the late hour, accommodations were made for all of us to spend the evening at the estate. I lapsed into a deep sleep and awoke in the morning wondering if the prior night's events had all been a dream. It was not until we gathered for breakfast that we realized we had taken part in one of the preeminent events in the history of the world—the passing of one of the greatest men who ever lived.

The General's passing turned the estate into a beehive of activity as Mr. Lear assumed the responsibility of all that needed to be accomplished: he wrote twelve letters that day announcing George's passing to everyone from President Adams and Alexander Hamilton to those who would serve as executors of the estate; a coffin needed to be ordered; and a funeral service must be planned. Later that evening the General's secretary asked my opinion on a fitting day to hold the funeral.

With these plans in place, I departed Mount Vernon on December 16 for I had

not been home for a couple of days. The next day, while I was at home, the coffin arrived at the estate from Alexandria. Tobias Lear supervised the solemn event of placing the General's body in the coffin at which point he clipped a small portion of his hair to be kept for posterity.

On December 18, family and friends gathered at Mount Vernon to say farewell to George Washington. With people still arriving, the noon service had to be moved to three in the afternoon. At that hour the procession moved from the mansion house to the old family tomb where the coffin was to be entombed. Recalling his military past, eleven guns fired a final salute on land, and additional guns were fired from a schooner in the Potomack. Servants Cyrus and Wilson led his horse, outfitted with his saddle, holster, and pistols, as we made our way south of the house. I was honored to be selected to walk with the family and close friends. Reverend Davis, who had presided at Nelly's wedding earlier in the year, read a simple service and had some short remarks at George's tomb. At long last my dear friend was laid to rest in the tomb that held so many family members who had gone before him. Following the service, I joined the rest of the mourners at a reception in the mansion house. How odd it was to be in the home without the imposing figure of George Washington there to greet us.

As an intimate friend of the family, I was invited to spend the evening, and when I awoke the morning of December 19, I had breakfast one last time with the family of my friend of nearly fifty years. On my trip north to Alexandria my mind wandered as I found myself retracing our lives and shared experience, from savage frontier fighting in the French & Indian War to the bloody battlefields of the American Revolution, from trips to the hot springs of Virginia to fox hunting on George's beautiful Mount Vernon estate. I recalled what a selfless man he was. He served his countrymen for sixteen years, eight at war and eight as our first president.

The day after Christmas, the official government service for Washington was held in the capital of Philadelphia. "Lighthorse" Harry Lee referred to his fellow Virginian as being "first in war, first in peace and first in the hearts of his countryman." All over the country, hundreds of memorial services celebrated the life and legacy of George Washington—yet his legacy was not complete.

Chapter Thirteen

As a young man, George Washington had once requested that an agent in London furnish him with busts of great military leaders of the past. He now joined those ranks as one of the great men to have lived. Artists would now carve his likeness in stone, and historians could begin to retrace his steps and record his story. The shelves of booksellers would, no doubt, be full of stories of his greatness.

A melancholy Christmas season eventually turned to a new year and century. As the young nation mourned the only father it had known, its inhabitants relished his two great accomplishments; resigning his military commission and his retirement from the presidency, all to withdraw to the peaceful life of a farmer. His life taught us to be steadfast and courageous in the face of overwhelming odds. In death, however, he had one final lesson.

Rumors of something momentous began to circulate when on January 10, 1800 George Washington's last will and testament was probated in Alexandria. His twenty-eight-page will, written entirely in his hand, did indeed contain directives that would elevate his reputation to new and uncharted territory. In item 1, George saw to it that his beloved wife of the past forty years inherited all that was due her.

He would have that no other way. He was as dedicated to her as she was to him.

Then in item 2 were instructions that no one expected: "Upon the decease of my wife it is my will & desire that all the slaves which I hold in my own right shall receive their freedom." George had never known a day without slaves. He became a slave owner at age eleven when he inherited "property" from his father's estate. In addition to land he was also given ten human beings. His views on slavery began to change during the Revolution and matured as he did, ultimately culminating in his final decision. Those freed would be compensated for the rest of their lives. Food, clothing, education or "to be brought up to some usefull occupation," and an array of other provisions were supplied to the freed slaves. Those too young or too old would benefit from a trust created by his will. It insured "that a regular and permanent fund be established for their support so long as there are subjects requiring it." He felt that a complicated set of issues prevented him from freeing "his people," as he often referred to them, prior to Martha's passing. She, however, took the step to free his slaves in 1801, a year before she passed.

Only one slave is mentioned by name in the will. His beloved valet William Lee, or Billy, is granted immediate freedom, a result of his attachment to General Washington and his service to him during the Revolutionary War. He was also the only freed slave to receive a lifetime annuity. As I write this letter, Billy is still living at Mount Vernon.

Although his health is failing he is still, for many, an important link to the past, to George Washington, and to all of us who fought so bravely during the War for Independence.

Washington once commented toward the end of his life that his association with slavery "has been the only unavoidable subject of regret." There are those who will always have difficulty reconciling his slave ownership, but surely the heavens looked kindly on his ultimate decision as stated in his last will and testament.

The final chapter in this incredible life was now closed. He was no different than any other man in a sense that he had faults and failings as we all did. He was seen by many as having almost god-like qualities in his dedication to his fellow man. On more than one occasion he placed his wealth, reputation, and his very life in harm's way so that all Americans could one day have the right to "life, liberty, and estate" as John Locke had so eloquently written in the previous century.

George Washington was many things to me—colonel, general, and president—but most of all he was my friend. As I close this long letter to you I would be remiss should I not inform you that I have transcribed my recollections while seated at and using the desk and chair Washington used during his presidency. They were a gift to me from George after his passing. My hope is that if someday in the future Mount Vernon becomes a shrine to him, these pieces of furniture will be returned and take their rightful place back in his study. When he bequeathed the desk and chair to me in his will, he wrote, "To my compatriot in arms, and old and intimate friend. . . ." It is a distinction I have worn like a badge of honor all of these years.

I am to you, Sir, as I was to him,

Your most humble and obedient servant,

James Craik

Looking out at a cold December sky from his Alexandria, Virginia home, Dr. Craik reflects on the many hours spent with his closest and dearest friend – from desperate frontier fighting in the French and Indian War to the General's peaceful passing at his beloved Mount Vernon estate. James Craik has recorded his recollections at the desk and chair bequeathed to him by George Washington in his will.

'Tis Well...

EPILOGUE

Like so many other patriots, James Craik may have otherwise been lost to time had it not been for his close relationship with George Washington and the important role he played in Washington's final scene. Two years his senior, he lived a long life, particularly by eighteenth and early nineteenth-century standards. He married Mariamne Ewell in 1760 and the couple had nine children, of whom one son was named for his father's close friend. He died at his residence in Alexandria, Virginia, on February 6, 1814, at age 84. He is buried at the Old Presbyterian Meeting House in Alexandria. It was said that "he had a healthy, cheerful old age.

Throughout the years, the subject of George Washington's medical treatment

Dr. Craik's signature acknowledges payment from his client and friend George Washington in 1788.

has been a topic of debate. Dr. Craik and Dr. Brown were in agreement on procedures while Dr. Dick, the youngest of the three men, differed in his opinion on what treatment to deliver the patient in his final hours. Dr. Brown later wrote to Dr. Craik that had they listened to Dr. Dick their good friend might still be alive. He went on to say that, governed by their knowledge at the time, they were justified in their actions. The suggested medical treatment of the day for quinsy was, in fact, bleeding.

During his first year as president of the new nation, President Washington purchased his "uncommon chair" from New York cabinet maker Thomas Burling. In the last year of his second term and in the nation's second capital, Philadelphia, he purchased his "tambour secretary," or writing desk, from cabinet maker John Aitken. These two pieces would be among the house full of belongings the Washingtons took back to Mount Vernon after his retirement from the presidency. Given to Dr. Craik by George Washington at the time of his passing, the "uncommon chair" and the writing desk would, ironically, return to Mount Vernon in the same year, but from different sources. In 1905 the General's desk came back to the estate directly from the heirs of Dr. Craik. The chair however, has a richer history. At some point the chair was given to President Andrew Jackson by one of Dr. Craik's granddaughters. Jackson used the chair at his Tennessee estate, The Hermitage. In 1905 it was returned to the Mount Vernon estate and they both took their rightful place back in the General's office. They can be seen today in George Washinton's private study at Mount Vernon.

Virtually all that we know of George Washington's final day comes from the accounts of Tobias Lear. He meticulously recorded his reminiscence with only slight deviations in those accounts. Dr. Craik, one of only a few eyewitnesses to the final scene, verified Lear's information by simply noting on December 15, the day after Washington's passing, the information was correct as far as he could recollect. It is interesting to note that on Christmas Day, seven days after the

funeral, Lear reentered the tomb to supervise the sealing of the lid of the lead inner lining of the coffin by the plumbers. He wrote that he "took a last look—a last farewell of that face, which still appeared unaltered. I attended the closing of the coffin—and beheld for the last time that face wh. shall be seen no more here; but wh. I hope to see in Heaven."

One of the many physicians serving under Dr. Craik's command in the Continental Army during the Revolution was Dr. James Thacher. Many years later he would write his reminiscence of the war. He recalled, "as a physician Dr. Craik was greatly distinguished by his skill and success, and his professional merits were highly and justly appreciated. In the various relations of private life, his character was truly estimable, and his memory is precious to all who had the happiness and the honor of his acquaintance."

I am certain George would have agreed!

'Tis Well...

This likeness of a contemporary image shows James Craik as a middle-aged man. He lived to age 84 and it was said that he had a healthy and cheerful old age.

'Tis Well...

Bibliography

Boatner, Mark M III. *Encyclopedia of the American Revolution*. Mechanicsburg, PA : Stackpole Books, 1966.

Fithian, Philip Vickers. *Journal and Letters of Philip Vickers Fithian: A Plantation Tutor of the Old Dominion, 1773-1774*. Edited by Hunter Dickinson Farish. Charlottesville: University of Virginia Press, 1947.

Flexner, James Thomas. *George Washington*. 4 vols. Boston and Toronto: Little, Brown and Company, 1969.

Freeman, Douglas Southall, *George Washington: A Biography*. 6 vols. New York: Charles Scribner's Sons, 1948-57.

Lear, Tobias. *Letters and Recollections of George Washington*. New York: Doubleday, Page & Company, 1906.

_____. *Washington Letters*. Rochester, New York: The Genesee Press, 1905

Thacher, James. *American Medical Biography*. Vol 1. New York: Da Capo Press, 1967.

Thompson, Mary. E-mail message to author. May 7, 2014.

Washington, George. *The Diaries of George Washington*. 6 vols. Edited by Donald Jackson And Dorothy Twohig. Charlottesville and London: University of Virginia Press, 1976

_____. *The Last Will and Testament of George Washington*. Edited by Dr. John C. Fitzpatrick. Virginia: The Mount Vernon Ladies' Association of the Union, 1939.

_____. *The Papers of George Washington: Colonial Series*. 10 vols. Edited by W.W. Abbot, Charlottesville: University of Virginia Press, 1983.

_____. *The Papers of George Washington: Retirement Series*. 4 vols. Edited by Dorothy Twohig, Philander D. Chase, and Beverly H. Runge, Charlottesville and London: University of Virginia Press, 1999.

_____. *The Papers of George Washington: Revolutionary War Series*. 12 vols. Edited by W.W. Abbott, Dorothy Twohig, and Philander D. Chase. Charlottesville: University Press of Virginia, 1985.

THE I knew George Washington SERIES

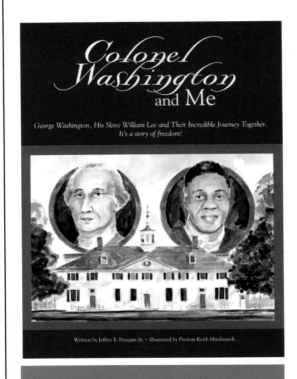

Colonel Washington and Me

In 1768 George Washington purchases a young man who was born into slavery. Washington has been a slave owner since age eleven. What develops is one of the more extraordinary relationships in American history. While most biographies on the first president mention the bond between George Washington and William Lee, *Colonel Washington and Me* is the first book dedicated solely to this story. The young reader travels through history as both men search for freedom on their incredible journey together.

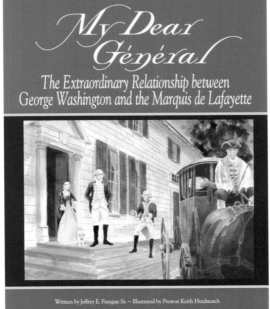

My Dear Général

My Dear Général - The Extraordinary Relationship of George Washington and the Marquis de Lafayette is the third in our unique series on the life of one of the preeminent personalities of the 18th Century, George Washington. For a childless Washington, Lafayette was the closest he came to having a son. For the orphaned Marquis, the tall, stately Virginian filled several roles in the young man's life – general, mentor, hero and most of all he was, as Lafayette referred to him, his "adoptive father."